JONATHAN D(

Gloria
(from *Missa Brevis*)

for SATB and Organ

EDITION PETERS
LEIPZIG · LONDON · NEW YORK

Gloria
(from *Missa Brevis*)

JONATHAN DOVE

4

8

-re, mi - se - re   -   re   no - bis.

-re, mi - se - re   -   re   no - bis.

-re, mi - se - re   -   re   no - bis.

-re, mi - se - re   -   re   no - bis.

Quo-ni-am tu so - lus Sanc - tus.
Quo-ni-am tu so - lus Sanc - tus.
Quo-ni-am tu so - lus Sanc - tus.
Quo-ni-am tu so - lus Sanc - tus.

Quo-ni-am tu so - lus Sanc-tus, tu so-lus Sanc-tus.
Quo-ni-am tu so - lus Sanc-tus, tu so-lus Sanc-tus.
Quo-ni-am tu so - lus Sanc-tus, tu so-lus Sanc-tus.
Quo-ni-am tu so - lus Sanc-tus, tu so-lus Sanc-tus.

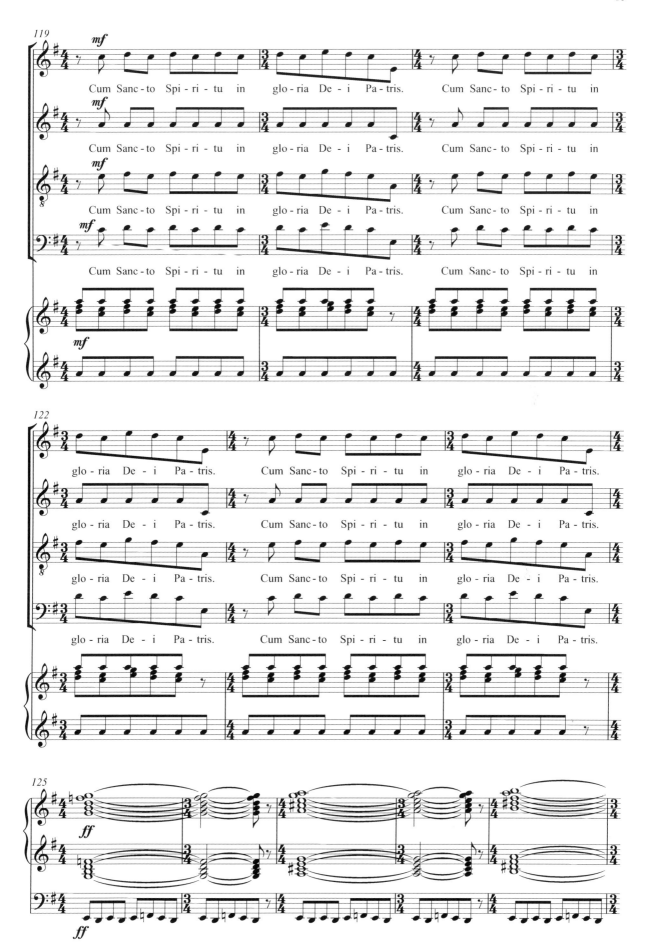

16

Jonathan Dove

Jonathan Dove (b. 1959) studied composition with Robin Holloway at Cambridge and worked as a freelance repetiteur, animateur and arranger. His first major projects came via Glyndebourne, including his breakthrough commission, the opera *Flight*, for Glyndebourne Touring Opera. Other operatic works include *The Adventures of Pinocchio*, *Swanhunter*, children's opera *The Hackney Chronicles*, *When She Died* – examining the response to the death of Diana, Princess of Wales – and *Man on the Moon*. Works for orchestra include the trombone concerto *Stargazer*, and *Moonlight Revels* for trumpet and saxophone. Dove was presented with the Ivor Novello Award for Classical Music in 2008, and in 2010 *A Song of Joys* opened the Last Night of the Proms.

Jonathan Dove (*1959) studierte bei Robin Holloway an der Universität Cambridge Komposition und arbeitete als freischaffender Korrepetitor und Arrangeur. Erste größere Werke entstanden in Zusammenarbeit mit dem englischen Glyndebourne Festival, darunter die Oper *Flight* – ein Auftragswerk der Glyndebourne Touring Opera, das ihm zum Durchbruch verhalf. Sein Opernschaffen umfasst außerdem *The Adventures of Pinocchio*, *Swanhunter*, die Kinderoper *The Hackney Chronicles*, *When She Died* – das die Reaktionen auf den Tod von Prinzessin Diana beleuchtet – sowie *Man on the Moon*. Zu seinen Orchesterwerken zählen das Posaunenkonzert *Stargazer* sowie *Moonlight Revels* für Trompete und Saxofon. 2008 erhielt Dove den Ivor Novello Award für klassische Musik, und 2010 bildete *A Song of Joys* den Auftakt zur „Last Night of the Proms".

EDITION PETERS GROUP

LEIPZIG · LONDON · NEW YORK

www.editionpeters.com

ISMN 979-0-57700-733-5

9 790577 007335